PETER PARKER™
SPIDER-MAN®

Contents

2002

Happy Christmas Michael lots of love Patricia, Madison, Kelin, Finn and Mistral xxxxx

Published by Pedigree Books Limited
The Old Rectory, Matford Lane, Exeter
EX2 4PS.
E-Mail: books@pedigreegroup.co.uk
Published in 2002.

Pedigree®

5.99

...WHY, STONE -- YOU LOOK LIKE YOU'VE SEEN A GHOST --

Chicken Soup for the Criminally Insane

Chicken Soup for the Criminally Insane ™

...restore your faith!

IT'S DAPHNE -- SHE'S BEEN KILLED IN A CAR CRASH!

OH, MY GOD!

BIG BEER

...NIGEL! WHAT ARE YOU DOING HOME SO EARLY --?

VERONICA! STONE!

...SINCE YOUR PLASTIC SURGERY, YOU'VE BEEN ACTING SO STRANGELY...

...BECAUSE HE'S AN IMPOSTOR --

OH, MY GOD -- CHASE!

PETER PARKER™:SPIDER-MAN®: Vol. 2, No. 22, October, 2000. (ISSN #1053-5667) Published by MARVEL COMICS, Bill Jemas, President; Bob Harras, Editor-in-Chief; Stan Lee, Chairman Emeritus. OFFICE OF PUBLICATION: 387 PARK AVENUE SOUTH, NEW YORK, N.Y. 10016. PERIODICALS POSTAGE PAID AT NEW YORK, N.Y. AND AT ADDITIONAL MAILING OFFICES. Published monthly. Copyright © 2000 Marvel Characters, Inc. All rights reserved. Price $2.25 per copy in the U.S. and $3.50 in Canada. Subscription rate for 12 issues: U.S. $27.00; foreign $39.00; and Canadian subscribers must add $10.00 for postage and GST. GST #R127032852. No similarity between any of the names, characters, persons, and/or institutions in this magazine with those of any living or dead person or institution is intended, and any such similarity which may exist is purely coincidental. This periodical may not be sold except by authorized dealers and is sold subject to the condition that it shall not be sold or distributed with any part of its cover or markings removed, nor in a mutilated condition. PETER PARKER SPIDER-MAN (including all prominent characters featured in this issue and the distinctive likenesses thereof) is a trademark of MARVEL CHARACTERS, INC. POSTMASTER: SEND ADDRESS CHANGES TO SPIDER-MAN, c/o MARVEL DIRECT MARKETING CORP./SUBSCRIPTION DEPT. P.O. BOX 1979 DANBURY, CT. 06813-1979. TELEPHONE # (203) 743-5331. FAX # (203) 744-9944. Printed in the U.S.A. MARVEL COMICS is a division of MARVEL ENTERPRISES, INC. Peter Cuneo, Chief Executive Officer; Avi Arad, Chief Creative Officer.

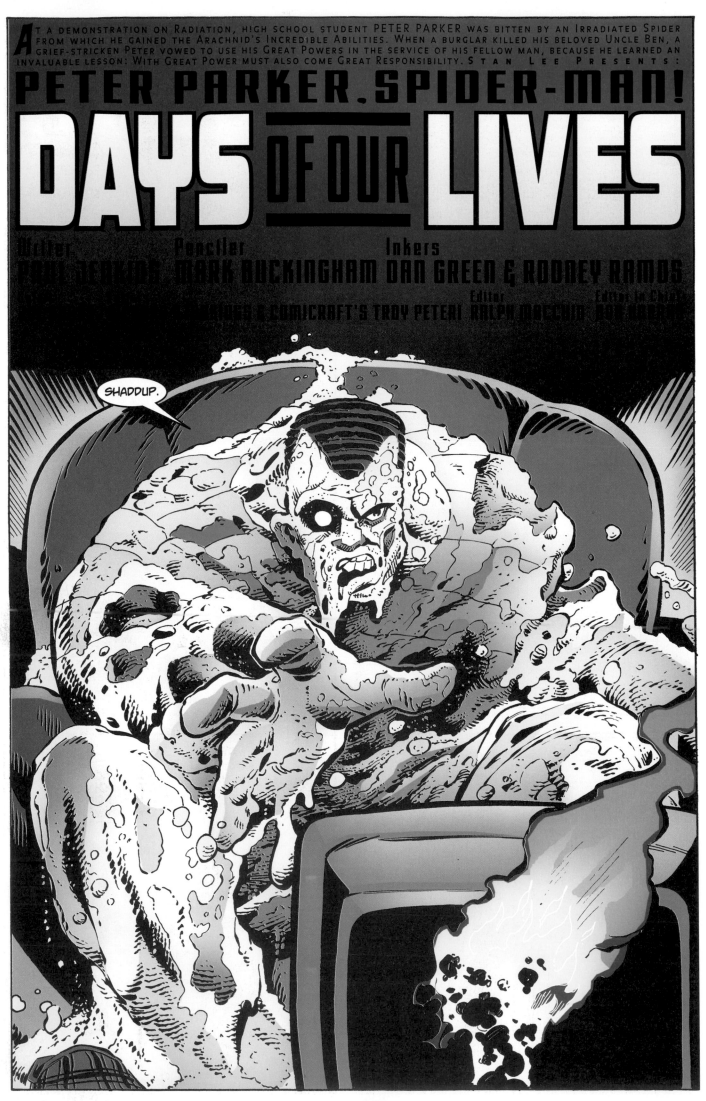

9

12

>AH-HAHH<... HEHH... THAT MAY'VE BEEN THE SINGLE FUNNIEST THING I EVER SAW IN MY *LIFE.* I C'N HARDLY *IMAGINE* WHAT HE'S DOING RIGHT NOW.

THE MIND BOGGLES.

YOU KNOW WHAT GOT ME? THAT REEDY LITTLE *VOICE* OF HIS! >AH-HEHH<... POOR GUY... HE SOUNDED LIKE HE WAS BEING *STRANGLED.*

HEY, HE'S NO PAVAROTTI -- BUT YOU GOTTA ADMIT, THE DUDE GIVES ONE HECK OF A *PERFORMANCE.*

DOES HE DO THIS SORT OF THING *OFTEN,* RANDY? RUN AROUND THE APARTMENT STARK *NAKED,* I MEAN?

I DUNNO. *YOU KNOW...* THAT WAS A SIDE OF HIM I'VE NEVER *SEEN* BEFORE --

HAR! HA HA HA HA!

coffee CAFE ·INC·

HEE! >SNORT!<

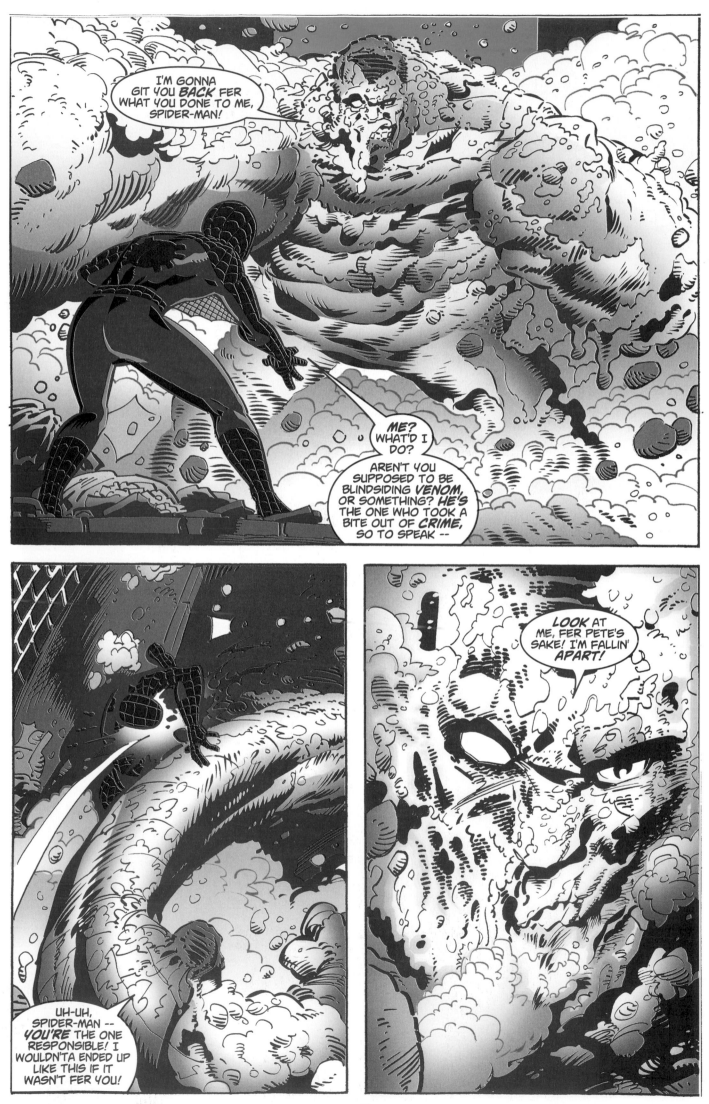

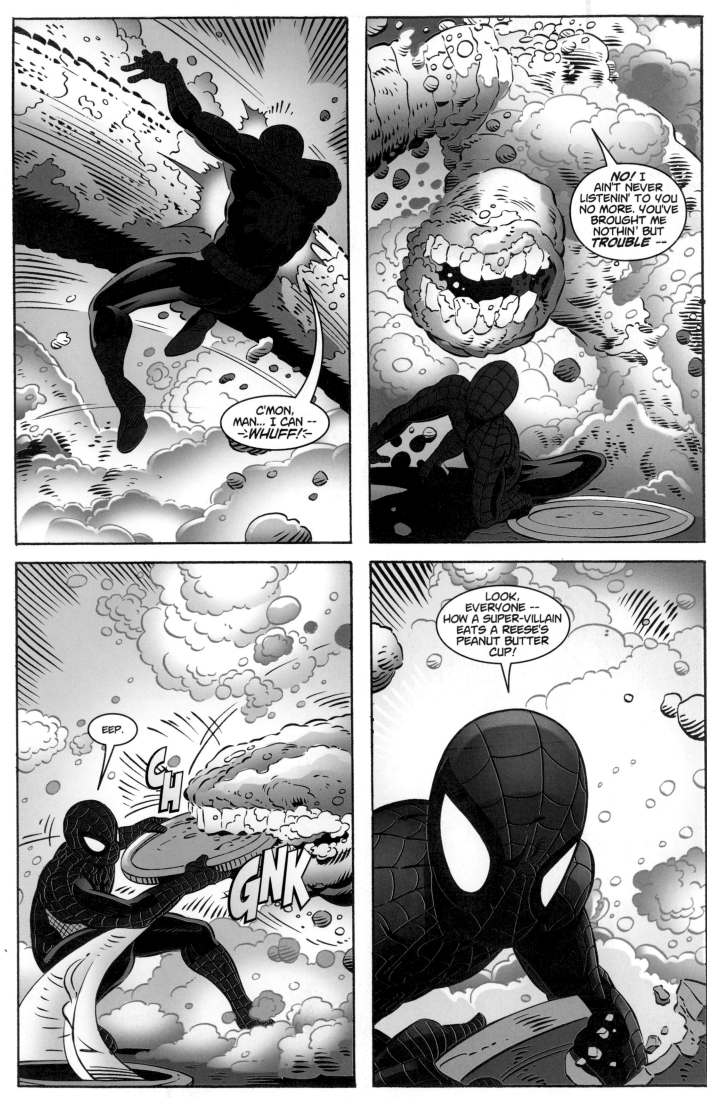

21

24

THE END

33

AND I'M CERTAIN WHEREVER HE IS, BEN IS PROUD TO BE THE UNCLE OF PETER PARKER.

THE END

AT A DEMONSTRATION ON RADIATION, HIGH SCHOOL STUDENT PETER PARKER WAS BITTEN BY AN IRRADIATED SPIDER FROM WHICH HE GAINED THE ARACHNID'S INCREDIBLE ABILITIES. WHEN A BURGLAR KILLED HIS BELOVED UNCLE BEN, A GRIEF-STRICKEN PETER VOWED TO USE HIS GREAT POWERS IN THE SERVICE OF HIS FELLOW MAN, BECAUSE HE LEARNED AN INVALUABLE LESSON: WITH GREAT POWER MUST ALSO COME GREAT RESPONSIBILITY. STAN LEE PRESENTS:

PETER PARKER SPIDER-MAN

THE SPIDER-MAN? OH YEAH, I SEEN HIM.

COUPLA TIMES, AS A MATTER OF FACT.

YOU KNOW HOW IT IS -- YOU WORK THE STREETS IN THIS CITY FOR TWENTY-FIVE YEARS, YOU PRETTY MUCH SEEN EVERYTHIN' AT THE END OF THE DAY...

BUT D'YOU KNOW WHAT'S REALLY AMAZING ABOUT THAT GUY: YOU ASK FIFTY DIFFERENT COPS ABOUT HIM AN' YOU'LL GET FIFTY DIFFERENT RESPONSES.

PETER PARKER™:SPIDER-MAN®: Vol. 2, No. 26, February, 2001. (ISSN #1053-5667) Published by MARVEL COMICS, Bill Jemas, President; Frank Fochetta, Senior Vice President, Publishing; Joe Quesada, Editor-in-Chief; Stan Lee, Chairman Emeritus. OFFICE OF PUBLICATION: 387 PARK AVENUE SOUTH, NEW YORK, N.Y. 10016. PERIODICALS POSTAGE PAID AT NEW YORK, N.Y. AND AT ADDITIONAL MAILING OFFICES. Published monthly. Copyright © 2000 Marvel Characters, Inc. All rights reserved. Price $2.99 per copy in the U.S. and $4.50 in Canada. Subscription rate for 12 issues: U.S. $27.00; foreign $39.00; and Canadian subscribers must add $10.00 for postage and GST. GST #R127032852. No similarity between any of the names, characters, persons, and/or institutions in this magazine with those of any living or dead person or institution is intended, and any such similarity which may exist is purely coincidental. This periodical may not be sold except by authorized dealers and is sold subject to the condition that it shall not be sold or distributed with any part of its cover or markings removed, nor in a mutilated condition. PETER PARKER SPIDER-MAN (including all prominent characters featured in this issue and the distinctive likenesses thereof) is a trademark of MARVEL CHARACTERS, INC. POSTMASTER: SEND ADDRESS CHANGES TO SPIDER-MAN, c/o MARVEL DIRECT MARKETING CORP./SUBSCRIPTION DEPT. P.O. BOX 1979 DANBURY, CT. 06813-1979. TELEPHONE # (203) 743-5331. FAX # (203) 744-9944. Printed in the U.S.A. MARVEL COMICS is a division of MARVEL ENTERPRISES, INC. Peter Cuneo, Chief Executive Officer; Avi Arad, Chief Creative Officer.

YEAH...RIGHT *HERE.* YOU WANT THE *TRUTH* ABOUT SPIDER-MAN, HUH? WELL, WHY DON'T YOU JUST TAKE A LOOK AROUND YOU FOR A SECOND.

YOU KNOW WHAT YOU *GOT* RIGHT HERE? YOU GOT A BUNCH OF HARD-WORKING, DEDICATED PROFESSIONALS WITH A SIX-WEEK BACKLOG OF HOMICIDES... ALL CHASIN' THEIR TAILS, AND FOR *WHAT?*

A PENSION AND A BLEEDING ULCER, *THAT'S* WHAT.

I'LL TELL YOU... WE GOT *MORE'N* ENOUGH TO DO AROUND HERE WITHOUT CHASING AFTER SOME LUNATIC THAT DON'T KNOW THE DIFFERENCE BETWEEN POLICE WORK AN' A *HOLE* IN THE GROUND --

TAKE THE OTHER DAY, FOR INSTANCE...

ME AN' YOULTON GET CALLED OUT TO PATEL'S DELI DOWN ON FIFTY-THIRD -- THERE'S BEEN A STANDOFF BETWEEN SOME UNIFORMED OFFICERS AND JOEY DAMIANI'S BOYS.

ACCORDING TO DISPATCH, SPIDER-MAN HAS CUT IN ON THE ACTION AND TAKEN THE BAD GUYS OUTTA THE PICTURE. I MEAN, ROUGHED 'EM UP *REAL* GOOD.

BOTTOM LINE: WE GOT FIVE WITNESSES TO WHAT HAPPENED, JOEY AN' HIS BOYS STUCK HALFWAY UP A STREET LIGHT OR OTHERWISE INCAPACITATED, AND ONE GRATEFUL VICTIM...

DET. PRATTON

"CUT AN' DRIED CASE, RIGHT? "WRONG."

POLICE STORY

PAUL JENKINS Writer JOE BENNETT Pencils
SANDU FLOREA Inks JOE ROSAS Colors
RICHARD S & COMICRAFT'S TROY PETERI Letters
AXEL ALONSO Editor JOE QUESADA Editor In Chief

some wise guys
for your collection.
Love, SPIDEY.

"WE ISOLATE THE SUBJECTS -- YOU KNOW... STANDARD PROCEDURE. I BRING JOEY OUT ON THE SIDEWALK AN' LEAVE HIS GOONS IN THE BACK OF AN RMV SO'S THEY CAN'T COMPARE NOTES.

"PROBLEM IS, JOEY KNOWS THE SCORE WHEN IT COMES TO SPIDER-MAN -- THE REAL *CLEVER* ONES ALWAYS DO..."

C'MON, DAMIANI...GIVE IT UP. YOU GOT TWO UNIFORMED OFFICERS SEEN YOU PULL A GUN ON MISTER PATEL. OR WERE YOU JUST SHOWIN' HIM HOW IT *WORKS* --?

I SWEAR, ME AN' THE BOYS, WE NEVER DONE *NUTHIN'*. WE JUST STOPPED OFF TO BUY SOME SMOKES AN' THE SPIDER-MAN ATTACKED US FOR NO REASON.

WE WAS TRYIN' TO *PROTECT* OURSELVES.

IS THAT *SO?* SO HOW COME YOUR CAR ENGINE WAS STONE *COLD* IF YOU JUST ARRIVED?

PTOO

HEY, THAT DON'T MEAN *NUTHIN'*. I AIN'T SAYIN' ANOTHER WORD UNTIL I SEE MY *ATTORNEY* --

"YOU SEE WHERE THIS IS *HEADED*, RIGHT? MEANWHILE, DETECTIVE PRATTON'S INSIDE TRYING TO PERSUADE THE OWNER TO PRESS CHARGES..."

LOOK, WE ALL *KNOW* WHAT WENT DOWN, MISTER PATEL. ALL YOU GOTTA DO IS MAKE THE I.D., OKAY? WE'LL TAKE IT FROM THERE --

WELL... I... UM...

41

AH, YES... I *REMEMBER* NOW! YOU SEE, THESE FINE GENTLEMEN -- THEY ARE *HEROES*!

IT WAS SPIDER-MAN WHO TRIED TO ROB MY STORE, AND THESE BRAVE MEN CAME TO MY AID. PERHAPS IF I OFFERED THEM A REWARD...?

SEE WHAT I *MEAN*? YOU GET A CASE THAT'S AIRTIGHT, AND YOU THROW THAT FREAK INTO THE MIX, AN' ALL OF A SUDDEN, YOU GOT A MESS ON YOUR HANDS.

WE GOT CRIMINALS SUING THE CITY FOR VIOLATION OF THEIR CIVIL RIGHTS, AN' GETTING OFF ON TECHNICALITIES ALL BECAUSE OF SPIDER-MAN'S INVOLVEMENT. HE'S MORE TROUBLE THAN HE'S *WORTH* --

THE SPIDER-MAN? YES, WELL... THAT'S A VERY INTERESTING QUESTION, ISN'T IT?

YOU KNOW, IN ALL HONESTY I'M NOT SURE *HOW* I FEEL ABOUT HIM.

"LET ME TELL YOU A STORY: A COUPLE OF YEARS AGO WHEN I FIRST MADE ASSISTANT D.A., A MANDATE CAME DOWN FROM THE MAYOR'S OFFICE THAT SPIDER-MAN WAS TO BE BROUGHT TO JUSTICE AT ALL COSTS.

"WE WORKED ON THE PROBLEM FOR A WHILE, AND ONE OF OUR JUNIOR ATTORNEYS CAME UP WITH A RATHER *CLEVER* IDEA:

"THIRTY-FOUR DETECTIVES AND POLICE MARKSMEN WAITED AND WAITED...ON THE COLDEST NIGHT OF THE YEAR...IN A DRIVING RAINSTORM. UNTIL FOUR IN THE MORNING."

AND, OF COURSE, SPIDER-MAN DIDN'T COME WITHIN *TEN MILES.*

"YOU MIGHT REMEMBER IT FROM THE NEWS REPORTS -- AT GREAT EXPENSE TO THE TAXPAYER, WE PROJECTED A GIANT SPIDER-SIGNAL IN THE HOPES HE WOULD TAKE THE BAIT AND COME RUNNING. AT WHICH POINT, WE WERE GOING TO RUN HIM IN.

43

"NATURALLY, THE MAYOR WAS ANNOYED THAT WE'D MADE SUCH OBVIOUS *FOOLS* OF OURSELVES, AND IMMEDIATELY BEGAN TRYING TO DISTANCE HIMSELF FROM HIS OWN DIRECTIVE.

"I RETURNED TO WORK AS USUAL AND PROMPTLY DISMISSED THE INCIDENT. UNTIL A FEW NIGHTS LATER AS I WAS ABOUT TO GET INTO MY CAR IN THE PRECINCT PARKING LOT..."

I WASN'T BORN *YESTERDAY*, LADY.

WELL, CAN YOU BLAME ME FOR TRYING, SPIDER-MAN? LET'S FACE IT: YOU'VE MADE A LOT OF PEOPLE VERY NERVOUS DOWN AT THE MAYOR'S OFFICE, AND I'M FEELING THE HEAT.

THEY WANT ME TO ASK YOU A FEW QUESTIONS ABOUT THE HEIST AT THE SECOND FEDERAL BANK LAST MONTH --

THAT WAS THE *RHINO* --

-- HEY! KEEP YOUR HANDS WHERE I CAN SEE THEM.

RELAX. I'M TRYING TO KILL *MYSELF*, NOT YOU.

44

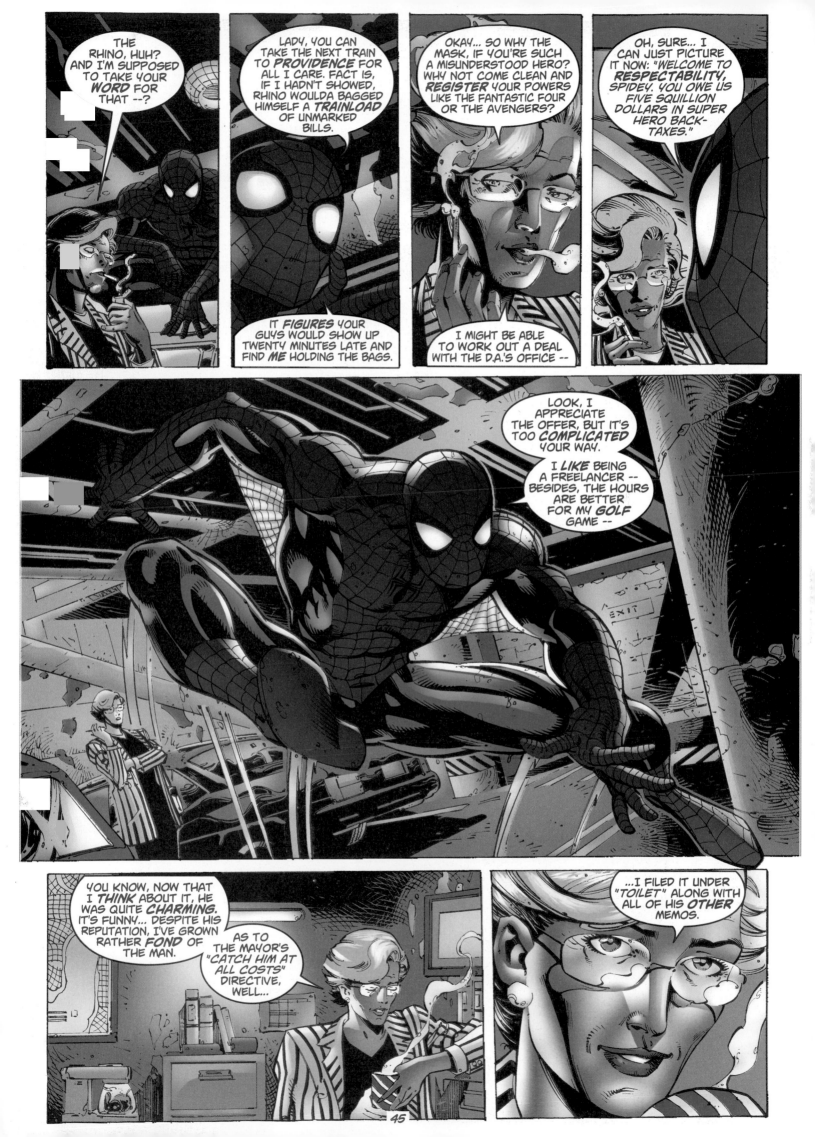

THE RHINO, HUH? AND I'M SUPPOSED TO TAKE YOUR *WORD* FOR THAT --?

LADY, YOU CAN TAKE THE NEXT TRAIN TO *PROVIDENCE* FOR ALL I CARE. FACT IS, IF I HADN'T SHOWED, RHINO WOULDA BAGGED HIMSELF A *TRAINLOAD* OF UNMARKED BILLS.

IT *FIGURES* YOUR GUYS WOULD SHOW UP TWENTY MINUTES LATE AND FIND *ME* HOLDING THE BAGS.

OKAY... SO WHY THE MASK, IF YOU'RE SUCH A MISUNDERSTOOD HERO? WHY NOT COME CLEAN AND *REGISTER* YOUR POWERS LIKE THE FANTASTIC FOUR OR THE AVENGERS?

I MIGHT BE ABLE TO WORK OUT A DEAL WITH THE D.A.'S OFFICE --

OH, SURE... I CAN JUST PICTURE IT NOW: "WELCOME TO *RESPECTABILITY*, SPIDEY. YOU OWE US FIVE SQUILLION DOLLARS IN SUPER HERO BACK-TAXES."

LOOK, I APPRECIATE THE OFFER, BUT IT'S TOO *COMPLICATED* YOUR WAY.

I *LIKE* BEING A FREELANCER -- BESIDES, THE HOURS ARE BETTER FOR MY *GOLF* GAME --

YOU KNOW, NOW THAT I *THINK* ABOUT IT, HE WAS QUITE *CHARMING*. IT'S FUNNY... DESPITE HIS REPUTATION, I'VE GROWN RATHER *FOND* OF THE MAN.

AS TO THE MAYOR'S "CATCH HIM AT ALL COSTS" DIRECTIVE, WELL...

...I FILED IT UNDER "TOILET" ALONG WITH ALL OF HIS *OTHER* MEMOS.

45

THE SPIDER-MAN IS A *LIABILITY*.

SEE THIS CHART? IT REPRESENTS HIS PATTERN OF OPERATIONS. MOSTLY REPORTED SIGHTINGS, THE OCCASIONAL BRUSH WITH LAW ENFORCEMENT. THE RED PINS REPRESENT MAJOR INCIDENTS.

I'VE MADE IT MY PERSONAL *CRUSADE* TO BRING THIS DANGEROUS VIGILANTE TO JUSTICE WHILE I'M IN OFFICE.

BECAUSE HE *KILLED* MY BEST FRIEND.

LOOK AT THESE TWO NUTBALLS -- THAT'S ME AND *GEORGE STACY.*

WE GRADUATED THE ACADEMY TOGETHER, WE WORKED A BEAT TOGETHER AND MADE DETECTIVE TOGETHER.

"GEORGE WAS THE BEST MAN I EVER KNEW -- BAR *NONE.*

"NEW YORK DIDN'T KNOW HOW LUCKY IT WAS TO HAVE SUCH A FINE MAN IN ITS SERVICE.

"HE WAS A SOLID, METHODICAL DETECTIVE -- ONE OF THE VERY BEST IN THE PRECINCT'S HISTORY.

"WE REMAINED FRIENDS LONG AFTER HE MADE CAPTAIN AND I WAS STILL JUST A LOWLY DETECTIVE.

"ONE DAY, WE CAME IN ON A FRACAS BETWEEN THE SPIDER-MAN AND ONE OF HIS SPARRING PARTNERS -- DOCTOR OCTOPUS.

"THEY WERE GOING AT IT ABOVE THE EDGE OF AN APARTMENT BUILDING IN A HIGHLY-POPULATED AREA. IT WAS OUR JOB TO CORDON OFF THE STREETS BELOW...

"...EXCEPT SOME LITTLE KID WANDERED TOO CLOSE TO THE ACTION JUST AS A PILE OF DEBRIS CAME DOWN...

"...AND POOR GEORGE FOUND HIMSELF IN THE WRONG PLACE AT THE WRONG TIME."

47

THE KID GOT AWAY WITH A COUPLE OF SCRAPES AND BRUISES -- MORE THAN COULD BE SAID FOR STACY, CRUSHED UNDER HALF A TON OF BRICK AND CEMENT.

ALL SIGNS INDICATED THAT HE WAS BARELY CLINGING TO LIFE.

"A FEW OF US RUSHED THE SCENE... THE SPIDER-MAN WAS NOW HOLDING GEORGE IN HIS ARMS. SOMEONE SCREAMED AT HIM TO PUT THE DYING MAN DOWN AND SURRENDER.

ALL I KNOW IS, WE FOUND GEORGE STACY DEAD ON TOP OF AN APARTMENT BUILDING ABOUT FIVE BLOCKS AWAY...

...REMOVED FROM THE SCENE BEFORE WE COULD GET HIM THE MEDICAL ATTENTION HE NEEDED.

"IT WAS THEN THE SPIDER-MAN SHOWED HIS TRUE COLORS -- MAYBE IT WAS TO SAVE HIS OWN HIDE, I DON'T KNOW. MAYBE GEORGE HAD FOUND OUT HIS SECRET IDENTITY OR SOMETHING."

THE SPIDER-MAN...? OH, THAT GUY IS *AMAZING*...

HERE, LET ME SHOW YOU SOMETHING I'VE BEEN WORKING ON: A FEW MONTHS AGO, WE MANAGED TO RECOVER A SAMPLE OF HIS WEBBING MATERIAL.

WE PRESERVED IT IN FORMALDEHYDE BEFORE IT COULD DETERIORATE. WE'RE HOPING TO DETERMINE ITS COMPOSITION, PERHAPS TRACE ITS MANUFACTURER THAT WAY.

ITS CHEMICAL MAKE-UP IS NOTHING SHORT OF *ASTOUNDING*. WE'VE FOUND TRACES OF SOME VERY EXOTIC PLASTICS, POLYCARBONS AND SO ON. EVEN MICROFILAMENTS OF WHAT APPEARS TO BE A *RUBIDIUM* COMPOUND.

WHOEVER CREATED THIS STUFF IS A SCIENTIFIC GENIUS, I CAN TELL YOU *THAT*. WE'VE RECOMMENDED A CANVASSING OF CHEMICAL LABORATORY WORKERS, PERHAPS EVEN DOCTORS OR VERY GIFTED STUDENTS.

OF COURSE, THE COMMISSIONER'S OFFICE HASN'T EVEN ACKNOWLEDGED RECEIVING OUR MEMORANDUM. THAT'S HOW WE *DO* THINGS AROUND HERE.

SPIDER-MAN? HEY, DON'T ASK *ME* ABOUT THAT GUY... ASK *PHILLIPS.*

HEY, *ROOKIE!* WHY DON'T YOU TELL EVERYONE WHAT HAPPENED WITH SPIDER-MAN THE OTHER WEEK?

I GOT A *BETTER* IDEA, JOVANOWSKI:

WHY DON'T YOU HAVE *ANOTHER* DONUT?

HEHH... DON'T MIND THE KID -- HE'S JUST *MODEST.*

"THE WAY I HEARD IT, IT HAPPENED OUT ON PATROL DOWN IN LITTLE ITALY. THE ROOKIE AND HIS PARTNER, HOPKINS, GOT CALLED OUT TO INVESTIGATE A DISTURBANCE IN BACK OF A RESTAURANT..."

"...THEY FOUND A **DISTURBANCE** ALL RIGHT!"

ME? LET ME TELL YOU ABOUT THE SPIDER-MAN: I REMEMBER THIS ONE DAY, A FEW YEARS AGO, WE GOT THIS CALL.

THERE'D BEEN SOME KIND OF DISTURBANCE OUT AT THE BROOKLYN BRIDGE...

"BY THE TIME I GOT THERE, THE PLACE WAS CRAWLING WITH ONLOOKERS AND REPORTERS. ALL THE TRAFFIC ON THE BRIDGE WAS SLOWED DOWN BY *RUBBERNECKERS*, RIGHT?

"AND THERE, HIGH UP ABOVE THE CITY NEAR THE TOP OF A BRIDGE SUPPORT, WAS THE MOST AMAZING THING I EVER *SAW...*"

"IT WAS THE SPIDER-MAN AND THE GREEN GOBLIN, GOING AT IT LIKE A COUPLE OF *MANIACS.* AND BELIEVE ME WHEN I SAY IT -- THOSE TWO WERE PULLING OUT *ALL* THE STOPS..."

JEEZ, SARGE... I HEARD ABOUT THESE GUYS IN THE ACADEMY, BUT I ALWAYS THOUGHT THEY WAS YANKIN' MY CHAIN --

YEAH, WELL... THIS *AIN'T* THE ACADEMY, SON. BETTER CALL DISPATCH AND TELL 'EM WE NEED BACKUP.

WHA

BLAM

GAHH!

WE GOTTA GET THESE PEOPLE OUT OF THE LINE OF FIRE... HEY, *RAMIRO* --!

WAY AHEAD OF YOU, SARGE! LET'S *MOVE,* PEOPLE --!

"I REMEMBER EVERYONE WAS UP IN ARMS ABOUT THAT. TURNS OUT THE GIRL WAS THE DAUGHTER OF CAPTAIN STACY -- AND SPIDER-MAN WAS NOW IMPLICATED IN THE DEATHS OF *BOTH* OF THEM.

"CAN YOU IMAGINE WHAT THE FAMILY MUST'VE BEEN GOING THROUGH? TO LOSE TWO PEOPLE LIKE THAT IN SUCH A SHORT PERIOD OF TIME?

"RIGHT AFTER THAT, THEY HAD TO BRING THE BOYFRIEND DOWN TO THE STATION FOR QUESTIONING...."

...IT'S JUST PROCEDURE, MISTER PARKER. CAN YOU TELL US YOUR WHEREABOUTS AT THE TIME OF THE, UH... INCIDENT?

YEAH, I WAS... I MEAN, I'M A *PHOTOGRAPHER*. I GUESS I DON'T HAVE MUCH OF AN ALIBI, SIR. I WAS WORKING FOR THE BUGLE THAT AFTERNOON.

MY *EDITOR* MIGHT BE ABLE TO VOUCH FOR ME --

THAT WON'T BE NECESSARY -- YOU'RE FREE TO GO. WHY DON'T YOU GO HOME AND GET SOME *SLEEP*, OKAY --?

"I WAS ON DESK DUTY THAT AFTERNOON. THAT POOR BOY, HE LOOKED LIKE HE HAD THE WEIGHT OF THE WORLD ON HIS SHOULDERS. IT WAS A REAL TRAGEDY..."

HEY, KID --!

LISTEN, SON... FOR WHAT IT'S WORTH, I *SAW* WHAT HAPPENED. I THINK YOU SHOULD KNOW, IT *WASN'T* THE SPIDER-MAN'S FAULT.

I KNOW IT DON'T MAKE NO DIFFERENCE, BUT HE TRIED TO *SAVE* YOUR GIRLFRIEND. I THINK HE TOOK IT REAL *PERSONAL* WHEN SHE GOT KILLED. BELIEVE ME, THAT GUY DID EVERYTHING HE *COULD*.

THANKS, SARGE...

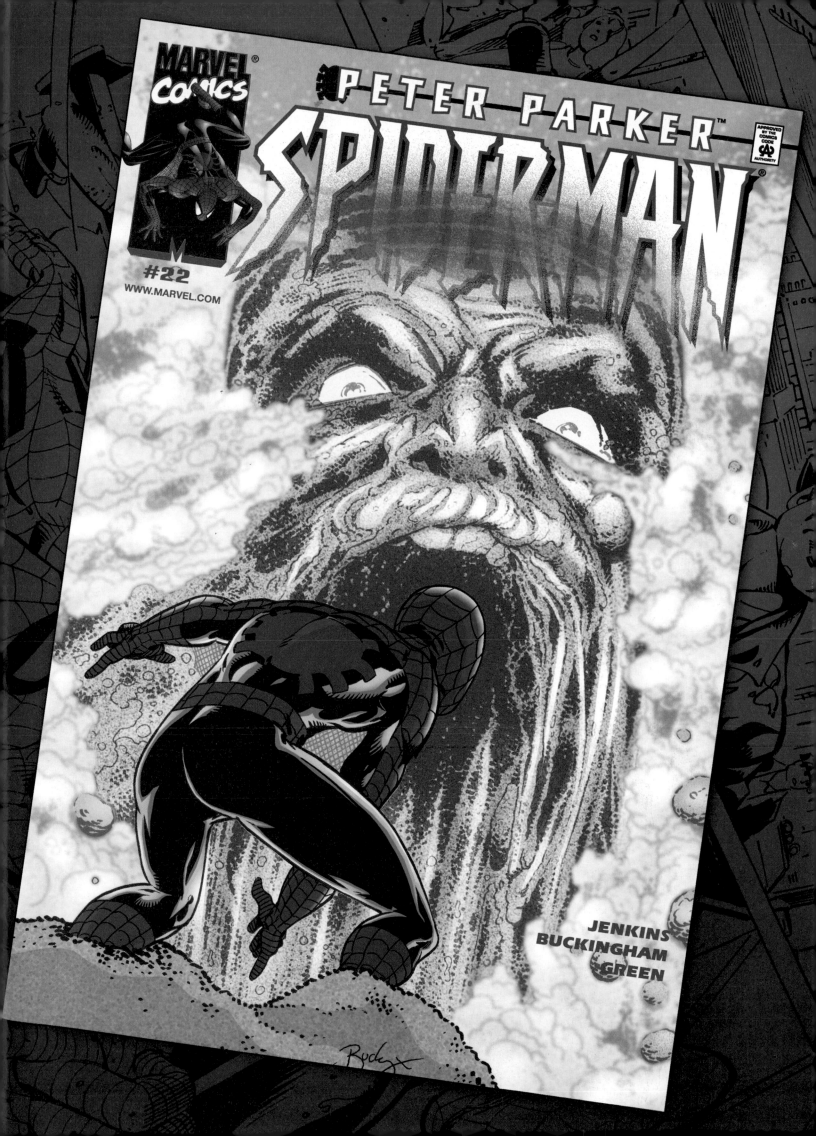